Changing Fashions
1800 = 1970

ELIZABETH ANN COLEMAN

THE BROOKLYN MUSEUM

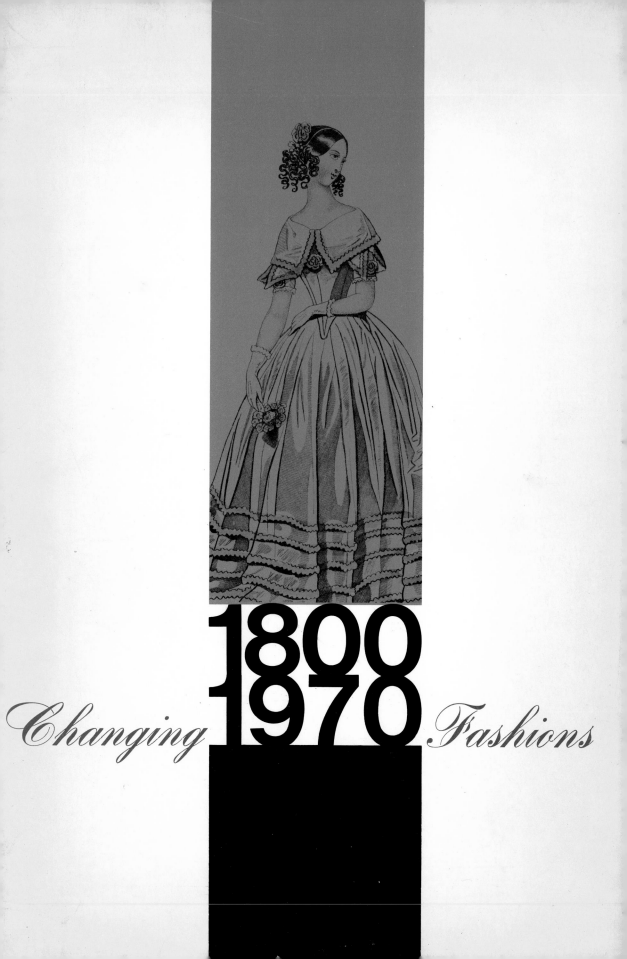

1800
1970
Changing *Fashions*

Introduction

This catalogue is being issued in conjunction with the inaugural installation in the newly designed Costume Galleries of The Brooklyn Museum. Entitled "Changing Fashions," it provides a survey of the clothes worn by American women from 1800 to 1970. Rather than considering the garments as isolated artifacts of bygone eras, an attempt has been made to place them in proper perspective in relation to contemporary social, economic, political, and technical developments.

A cursory study of styles in clothing can be deceptive. Changes of fashion in garments are written about more than in any other field of design. It is seemingly easy to trace the introduction of a mode, but it is practically impossible to proclaim its demise. The state of communications; the age and situation of the wearer; economic, social, and geographical factors all determine the brevity or longevity of a fashion. A quote from the November 1849 issue of *Godey's Ladies Book* reflects this awareness: "We present some of the newest and most graceful Parisian costumes which will probably be in vogue with us next season. It is undeniable that Americans are just one season behind the gay capital of France, in the style of their dress, furniture and equipage, and that much of it is so unsuited as never to be seen here at all."

The Costume Galleries were evolved over a period of years from an idea originally suggested by Thomas S. Buechner, former director of the Museum. Generous sponsorship was provided by Robert E. Blum, the Avalon Foundation, the New York Foundation, and the Shannon Rodgers Foundation. A series of designs and subsequent modifications were issued by our untiring architect, Paul Heyer. The myriad preparations were ably carried out by a most dedicated staff and a group of unfailing departmental volunteers: Adrienne Drucker, my secretary; Dassah Saulpaugh, my predecessor; Helene Von Rosenstiel, my assistant; Mary Buechner, Evelyn Jane Coleman, Lisa Cook, Alberta Darby, Anne Estern, Adele Filene, and Marilla Palmer. The entire project was supervised by J. Stewart Johnson, Curator of Decorative Arts. To all of these, and to many others who generously contributed their time and skills, I extend my sincerest gratitude.

ELIZABETH ANN COLEMAN
*Associate Curator in Charge
of Costumes and Textiles*

Evening Dress

AMERICAN ABOUT 1805

After the major social and political upheavals of the late eighteenth century, the dawn of the nineteenth was relatively quiet. In fashion, trends conceived in the waning years of the old century were carried into the new. In dress design, round gowns were popular. A round gown is tubular and must be slipped over the head; it looks like a lengthened chemise that has been drawn in below the bustline. Linear and unornamented, these stark dresses made an astonishing contrast to the curvaceous ruffled and ribboned open robes (dresses open in front over underlayers) of prerevolutionary France and America.

Elaborately woven muslins, usually white, silks in soft pastel shades, and gaudy chintzes were the fabrics most often used. Between 1803 and 1806 gowns with trains were given prime exposure in fashion periodicals. An example is this hand-stitched dress of gunmetal gray silk with a weighted and double-lined trapezoidal-shaped train. The bodice flaps down in front and must be secured over the bust with ties around the high waist and straight pins at the shoulder. It has a linen lining, with tabs to be pinned. Undergarments were kept to a minimum, the chemise being often the only undergarment worn.

Gift of Charles Blaney   26.495

Fashion plate from *Mirror de la Mode,* 1803.

Day Dress

AMERICAN ABOUT 1813

A cotton fabric printed with vivid yellow dots on a bold blue ground was used for this New England day dress. Although textile mills had been established early in this country, particularly in Massachusetts, considerable quantities of inexpensive dress goods continued to be imported from England, and it is sometimes impossible to distinguish the native from the imported products. An English textile merchant's log for the years 1807–09 includes notations on the tribulations associated with the production and distribution of assorted small-figured prints. An entry for September 2, 1809, reads: "Supply us with 10 times the quantity of green chintz you have lately done. The patterns Black olive & yellow & Black olive yellow & Blue you may do 100 ps No 1 SS [100 pieces of 'Super Super' grade cloth] taking care the printing is well done & dont exceed 100 ps as we do not think the style will sell to any great extent." Ironically, the prints made popular during this era were used extensively throughout the century.

This dress has a high double-ruff neckline and a slightly flared skirt with fullness gathered to the back. The diamond-shaped bodice back construction dates back to the late eighteenth century.

Gift of Miss Florence Inniss   70.123.1

Day Dress

AMERICAN ABOUT 1815

For all functions and seasons, fashion in the first two decades of the nineteenth century usually called for white gowns. Accessories — shoes, gloves, shawls, and spencers (a short-waisted jacket) — frequently provided the only touches of color. The preference for white was the result of the enthusiasm for emulating the ancients, a phenomenon that reached its zenith from 1790 to 1810. Greek and Roman marble sculpture influenced the way dresses were draped and the lack of color. This day dress has a white muslin ground embellished with blue and cream sprigs woven with wool yarns.

The clinging tubular shape popular in this period meant that ladies could no longer conceal their pockets in the traditional manner, secured to the waistband and worn under the skirt. The pocket was now carried in the hand instead. Retaining its former shape, it was given a drawstring closing and christened a "ridicule."

The fluctuating waistline ascended to its highest point about 1815, just as sleeves reached their greatest length.

Gift of The Jason and Peggy Westerfield Collection   69.2.4

Fashion plate from *Costume Parisien,* 1814.

Evening Dress

PROBABLY FRENCH   ABOUT 1820

A dress remarkably similar to this one represented "L'Elégance en 1820" in a group of contemporary fashion plates reprinted in France early in the twentieth century, except that our gown has short sleeves. However, the Museum received one removable long sleeve with the garment, as lavishly embellished as the one in the print. By the addition of the long sleeves, which were secured to the cuffs of the puff sleeves, the wearer could transform the dress to suit the occasion or the temperature. Gowns of this kind were recommended for year-round use, as afternoon, evening, dinner, ball, or opera attire. The cut of the dress is typical of the period: square neck, medium-high bodice, two sleeve lengths, tubular skirt with a slight flare at the hem and all the fullness gathered to the back. What is remarkable is the quality of the decoration. Worked on a fine white cotton ground, it includes petal puffs of sheer mull, fagoting, white-on-white satin stitch sprigs, and a variety of needlework lace insertions as delicate as snowflakes.

   Metal hooks, introduced in 1815, are secured in stitched eyelets down the back of the bodice, and a tape drawstring at the neck fits the dress to the form. Modish accessories include a fine green cashmere shawl patterned with colored wool embroidery and lemon yellow kid slippers to match the long gloves.

A. Augustus Healy Fund   26.211a-b

Fashion plate: "L'Elégance en 1820."

Ball Gown

ENGLISH 1828–30

Sir Walter Scott and other writers of romantic tales attracted an avid readership in the early nineteenth century. Stories of medieval chivalry aroused in female readers a desire to imitate their heroines in dress, but the romantic gowns they concocted took current modes into account. Fashionable short puffed sleeves were left intact, but long pendant cuffs were added, and a hemline might be caught up to expose another layer. For this period sleeves were the important feature. Since about 1820 they had been growing fuller by the year until they reached "gigot" (leg of mutton) or "imbecile" proportions (the fullness is lower in the "imbecile" sleeve and more evenly distributed). To support these ballooning sleeves, special down-filled pads were worn; they were tied by tapes to the gown at the shoulder and looked not unlike the full puff sleeves of this gown as seen through transparent gauze oversleeves. This sleeve treatment, padded and transparent, was modish between 1825 and 1835. Our ball gown, of sprigged pink silk taffeta, has a deep hemline "rouleau" with satin trim applied in the manner of renaissance slashes. The reticule (formerly known as a "ridicule") matches the gown.

Our mannequin wears an "Apollo's Knot" coiffure. These elaborate arrangements, which required that hairpieces be added to the wearer's own hair, were garnished with jewels or pearls, feathers, flowers, and ribbons.

H. Randolph Lever Fund   71.76a–c

Portrait of Mrs. Robert Donaldson by George Cooke, c. 1832. Gift of the Haskell Estate, 43.210.

Day Dress

AMERICAN   ABOUT 1837

By 1837, the year the young Queen Victoria ascended the throne of England, two noteworthy alterations were underway in dress design. One was the deflation of sleeve fullness; first gathered in at the shoulder and then by bands down the arm, fullness was squeezed from both ends of the sleeve toward the middle. The other change was the expansion of the circumference of the skirt. In order to follow fashion's dicta regarding breadth, more and more petticoats were added to the daily toilette.

The *Ladies Cabinet* of January 1837 states that "a 'robe de chambre' is indispensable in home costume, and is often more expensive than a 'toilette de soiree'. Those most in favor at the present, are of cashmere with applications of velvet. . . . In order to render the costume complete, there must be a pretty little mourning [*sic*] cap." Our day dress is of floral-printed challis trimmed with green silk. Essential accessories were a cap, with or without a "caul" or crown, bedecked with simple ribbons or the elaborate knotted-ribbon trim called bullion; a "pelerine," the cape-like collar making its final appearance in this shoulder-broadening form; and finally mittens.

Gift of Mrs. Harold Szold   57.61

Promenade Dress

AMERICAN ABOUT 1839

Fashionable ladies of the 1830's insisted on dress materials printed in bright colors and bold patterns. Designs that appeared to be three-dimensional, with a colorful and intricate primary motif set against a monochrome background of moss or vine pattern, were admired. The *Ladies Cabinet* for November 1839 noted that there was "an immense variety of rich silks . . . both plain and figured in such rich and striking patterns, that one might well fancy they were embroidered."

Silk dresses were much favored and were recommended for promenade, dinner, evening, and ball wear. The length and shape of the bodice fluctuated, our example being termed "half high" and "round" because it is not pointed at the waist. The draping of the bodice across the bust was designated as a "corsage à la Sevigné" or "Maintenon" or any one of several other French court ladies of the eighteenth century. Sleeve fullness at the shoulder is laid in flat pleats, and the wrist is form-fitting, thus confining the fullness to the area around the elbow.

Gift of The Jason and Peggy Westerfield Collection 69.2.9

Fashion plate from *Ladies Cabinet,* c. 1839.

Morning Visiting Dress

AMERICAN ABOUT 1843

Fashion and social class are sometimes related in subtle and amusing ways. For ladies of the 1840's, sleeve design served to point up social position. "Plain, tight, long sleeves" were "coming in again, decidedly, notwithstanding all that has been said against them," noted a contemporary fashion journal. These form-fitting sleeves, "sadly disadvantageous to some figures," were set in off the shoulder and on the upper arm, making it impossible to raise the arm above ninety degrees. As a result, those whose lives demanded the slightest exertion were excluded from participation in this dress vogue. For those fortunate ladies whose winter activities encompassed nothing more energetic than sketching, reading, needlework, and visiting, a "carriage dress of dark drab satin perkin; fitting close to the figure, the waist . . . long and pointed" would be suitable.

Such a dress is our one-piece gown of striped red, purple, and light gray satin. The gauged (evenly gathered) waist of the skirt is fitted to the deep point of the tubular corsage (bodice), while the cape-like "bertha" emphasizes the low shoulder line. A contemporary English fashion plate shows a more elaborate version with flounces around the hem, but it has an identical corsage "trimmed with a pelerine of a round form, set on just above the shoulders."

It is interesting that the American arbiter of fashion, *Godey's Ladies Book,* makes no note of fashion changes for two and a half years beginning in July 1844 except to restate that there is none.

Gift of Miss Annie M. Colson   29.1159

Fashion plate from *Ladies Cabinet,* November 1842.

Ball Gown

AMERICAN   ABOUT 1851

World attention in 1851 was focused on the Great Exhibition in the Crystal Palace in London, an international display of arts, crafts, and manufactures sponsored by Prince Albert, Queen Victoria's consort. All manner of textiles and dress accessories were included in the exhibition, and, as the following partial list shows, the same might be said for lost articles:

271 handkerchiefs
183 brooches
118 parasols
 28 pairs of gloves
 14 silk and 9 cotton umbrellas
 14 shawls
  3 fans
  2 coats
  1 petticoat

An American lady crossing the Atlantic for the exhibition might have packed this ball gown of cream satin embroidered in a sprig motif with gold and silver wire coils. Bodice and skirt are joined together, the point of the bodice lying over the skirt in front. The bodice is boned with whale baleen, three strips in front, one under each arm, and another at the back closing.

The specifications for skirt construction were drawn up in *Godey's*: "Skirts are still made full and long; they are very little trimmed in heavy materials . . . Skirts are gauged [evenly gathered], instead of being plaited [pleated] — unless in brocades or heavy satins . . . When the bodice is pointed . . . the skirt is gauged evenly and placed upon a band, not 'turned in' at the top to fit the points, which come over it."

Gift of the Methodist Episcopal Home for the Aged   55.203

Ball Gown

AMERICAN   ABOUT 1858–59

The numerous mid-Victorian journals that dispensed fashion advice to their feminine readers regularly predicted the demise of the crinoline frame (these wire cage-like skirt supporters were so named because the earliest ones had been made with horsehair or "crin de cheval"). *Godey's* in March 1860 joined the bandwagon in recounting a Parisian report that "the Imperial fiat has gone forth as regards crinoline, as I observe some of our 'elegantes' already walking up and down the Champes Elysees a la Dorothy Draggletail, performing the ignominious chore of street sweeper, with silks at twelve shillings a yard. Rather an expensive broom you will say. . . . The fact of several of the celebrated crinoline makers taking out patents at the present moment is also a favorable sign." Favorable indeed, for in fashionable circles the crinoline frame was to last another three-quarters of a decade.

Another nineteenth century invention, and a more enduring one, was the sewing machine. The small family version was immediately and universally accepted in the late 1850's, and the chain stitch began to appear in garments of all sorts (the familiar lock stitch was a later modification).

By 1858–60 the double-flounced skirt had superceded the multi-flounced skirt popular throughout the previous decade, but, as the fashion periodicals illustrate, the diameter of the skirt reached its greatest extent as the number of flounces diminished. This brown, black, and pearl white brocaded taffeta dress has a waist measurement of 23 inches and a hemline circumference of 168 inches. Accessories are a headpiece made of stitched shells and a parure (set) of gold-mounted cameos: necklace, brooch, and bracelet.

Gift of The Jason and Peggy Westerfield Collection   69.2.17

Sketch from *Harper's Bazar,* July 25, 1857.

Day Dress

AMERICAN ABOUT 1862

"The colors of the season for dresses are more sober and plainer taste has certainly taken the place of the flashy character that has been so conspicuous of past years," noted a fashion journal of the early 1860's. Bearing out this description is a day dress of brocaded silk taffeta with a lavender and gold Persian leaf motif on an olive green ground. The bodice, lined with a twill-woven muslin and boned in front only, is fastened with hooks and eyes under the sham button closing. Shaped pagoda sleeves, lined with white china silk, cover undersleeves, or "engageants." These undersleeves, which match the collar, became an essential accessory about 1851 and remained so for over twenty years, varying only in shape and fabric. When engageants were introduced, ladies were advised that "buttons will be found more convenient than cuff pins in a hurried toilet and elastic bands will fasten them above the elbow. If they are tied [sewn] in they cannot be so easily changed." "Lace should never be worn with a morning dress. A long, full sleeve of plain cambric or jaconet muslin, gathered into a broad band of open stock or embroidered cambric, is the most suitable for a dressing gown or any other home costume. Rich lace or muslin may be worn at dinner or in the evening."

The separate skirt has a pleated waistline and a seam pocket on the right side. Ruched trim of plain olive taffeta with lavender rosettes completes the gown. A beige wool tape was attached to the hemline to prevent wear.

Gift of The Jason and Peggy Westerfield Collection   69.2.20

Fashion plate from *Journal des Demoiselles,* September 1861.

Afternoon Dress

AMERICAN ABOUT 1865–67

Almost as if the fall of Dixie and the eclipse of the French Second Empire had signaled a change in its fortunes, the voluminous crinolined skirt fell limp. But designers who were accustomed to expending great yardage in a skirt were not to be stopped; they merely rearranged the fullness by drawing it to the back, reviving first the tournure (a cushion worn in the small of the back to puff out the skirt) and later the bustle. An English publication of 1867 lamented that "it has become the fashion for reputable Englishwomen to paint their faces and tint their eyelids, to wear false hair and supposititious tournures. Present fashions are hideous."

With a more positive outlook, the fashion editor of *Godey's* reported in April 1867: "A new material for evening wear is either white or black grenadine spotted over with large tufts of silk of every imaginable color. It is very effective and pretty." The grenadine (open weave) fabric used for this dress is pina cloth (made from pineapple fibers) of a leno weave with dobby-woven leaf motif (leno weaving gives strength and firmness to open-weave cloth, and the dobby attachment permits the weaving of small figures which are beyond the range of most simple looms). The leaf motif is reminiscent of classical designs, for designers of the late 1860's revived and interpreted the pseudo-classical gowns of the early years of the nineteenth century: "the short waists and scant skirts adopted by many, are suggestive of the days of Josephine." The bodice has a shirred yoke and two-piece sleeves, a style which had been adopted about 1863 from the cut of men's coat sleeves. Because the fabric is transparent, an attached sham camisole is provided, while the attached skirt, decorated "en tablier" (to resemble an eighteenth century open robe) has a gauze lining that allows the decorative detailing of the petticoat to be glimpsed.

Gift of Mrs. G. H. Marchant   61.17.2

Walking Suit

AMERICAN ABOUT 1870

The wearer of this outfit must have heeded the fashion advice offered by *Godey's* during the second half of 1869. "For walking suits, nothing can be made too elaborate, they are the costume now worn for visiting and promenade, and consequently are made of the richest and most costly fabrics." "There is no article of dress which we could better recommend to our readers to purchase, which is always worn, looks well, and lasts a lifetime, than a black lace point, these can be purchased in real or imitation, as the means of the purchaser admits." And for the tailoring details: "Corsages [bodices] are of medium length and round at the waist. Shoulder seams are short and high. The two darts in each front are short, but made very deep, to make an easy tapering shape . . . the high neck and ruche is most becoming, and does not look old fashioned. Sleeves of street dresses are easy fitting, coat-shaped. They have bows at the elbow and broad trimming at the wrist . . . The round pannier puff is not so pretty as the new bee pannier. This has two wings, pointed and open to the belt behind [the overskirt of our dress combines elements of both puff and bee pannier] . . . trained skirts of silk or muslin are flounced almost to the belt. These flounces are either bias or straight, slightly gathered or box plaited [pleated]. They are pinked out or bound with satin. It is no use to say we are tired of flounces, they were never so much worn as at present, there are literally ruffles upon ruffles."

This three-piece garment probably represents an early attempt at ready-made clothing, the advantages of which were thus described: "Ladies frequently inquire whether it is better to purchase ready-made clothing or to buy the material and have it made home by a hired seamstress. There is probably a greater outlay of money in buying ready-made garments, but there is no danger of loss of material, badly fitting clothes and none of the worry with workwomen."

Dick S. Ramsay Fund   56.129.100

Visiting Dress

AMERICAN   ABOUT 1875

The downfall of the full crinoline frame was brought about by dress designs that required fullness in back only. The new solution was the bustle, which looks not unlike a crinoline frame that has been sliced in half. To secure the bustle in place across the back of the wearer, the reinforced bands were frequently attached to a fabric apron with a laced center panel that allowed for adjustments of the back arc. The bustle merely supported the gown, it did not puff it out. Careful placing of tape ties on the underside of the skirt permitted the wearer to adjust the number of puffs and the amount of fullness.

This two-piece dress of lime and emerald green silk faille was worn over a bustle and has adjustable ties that draw back the fullness. The outfit also boasts a ruffle on the underside of the hemline. Known as a "dust ruffle," it was both functional and decorative. It could be easily removed for laundering after collecting ground dirt, and it was attractive to view when the train was pushed aside.

Undergarments, which had proliferated in number over the last seventy-five years, could be purchased or made in matched sets. An ensemble was composed of chemise, corset cover, drawers, petticoat, and nightgown. A lady first put on drawers and chemise, then the corset and corset cover, and finally the petticoat(s).

Gift of Mrs. G. H. Marchant   61.17.3

Sketch from *Harper's Bazar,* May 19, 1877.

Dinner Dress

AMERICAN   ABOUT 1877

The 1870's were a decade of economic instability and political and social reform in both Western Europe and the United States. The ferment of the times may well have been reflected in dressmaking, for this decade witnessed some of the most elaborately contrived dresses of the century. Most dressmakers seem to have regarded a symmetrical design or an unadorned area as heresy.

Silver blue and pale peach striped silk was pleated, puffed, knotted, looped, twisted, and draped to confect this dinner dress. Further elaboration was added in the form of gold silk taffeta ruching, machine-made lace, silk tulle, gold-beaded buttons, and frosted-glass baubles. The application of ruching and lace around the lower edge of the peplum nicely disguises the fact that skirt and bodice are separate.

This dress also illustrates the eclectic taste of the late Victorians. Neckline, sleeve length, and cuff treatment are based on mid-eighteenth century models, the design of the skirt on late seventeenth century examples, and the slashed sleeves on sixteenth century garments.

Gift of Mrs. C. D. Waters   45.168.4a-b

Promenade or Visiting Dress

AMERICAN ABOUT 1882

For a period of about five years, from 1877 to 1882, the extravagant projection of the bustle was dropped and bodice and skirt were made in a single unit. The fashion editor of *Peterson's* in January 1881 wrote from Paris: "I cannot remember a season, when there has been such a total change in important points in fashions as in this. Dull silks have been replaced by satin; warm, rich colors have taken the place of dull faded tints, so long popular nor are ladies' skirts strapped back so as to hinder their movements. The low neck corsage [bodice] is less and less worn, indeed, except at large parties, or balls, the square corsage and lace sleeves are in favor. The corsage is made dressy with lace, tulle, etc. For driving, or demi-toilette dresses, the favorite is the Princesse, or Gabrielle, cut in two materials, the front differing from the back. . . . The back and train of the dress (for the Princesse shape requires a train) are made of either velvet or brocade, the front being of satin, either shirred or embroidered."

This gown and hat ensemble are of gold and pink satin. The pink front panel of the gown is shirred, and pink bows are used to unite the two colors in a decorative manner. Stylistically the dress is as close to eighteenth century models as nineteenth century designers were able to fabricate, with open robe draped as a "polonaise" over the hips, "stomacher" or front panel inserted into the bodice, and undercoat (petticoat).

Gift of Miss Evelyn Eaves. Presented in memory of Elizabeth Predmore Eaves by her daughters, Evelyn Eaves and Emma Eaves Alyea   40.421a–b

Walking Suit

AMERICAN   ABOUT 1885

The admiration for overstuffed upholstered furniture was carried over to feminine attire in the 1880's. Observing the dress styles of the period, one is struck by the fact that the extension of the bustle created a silhouette strikingly similar to that of a chair. Little or no difference can be discerned in the use of fabrics and trimmings in dressmaking and in upholstery. In the case of millinery and dress accessories, feathers were applied decoratively rather than used as stuffing.

This fall walking suit is of heavy cream wool flannel edged with a substantial light brown hemp braid. Although designed to be worn over a corset, the bodice too is liberally boned. The skirt is made in two sections: an underskirt and a draped overskirt caught up in the center back by hooks, a feature which enhances the bustle effect while giving a fishtail outline. Elastic tapes uniformly placed down the inside back draw in the fullness.

The outfit is accessorized with a cream beaver toque, a hat style popular during the 1880's, and a tippet and matching muff of gull feathers.

Gift of Mrs. C. G. Mourraille   58.12.1

Fashion plate from *Journal des Demoiselles,* August 1, 1882.

Ball Gown

FRENCH   ABOUT 1892

By the 1890's American heiresses were swarming to Europe with two objects in mind: a titled husband and a wardrobe from the House of Worth, Rue de la Paix 7, Paris. The magnetism of Worth gowns seems to have inhered not in their designs but in the fact that everybody who was anybody wore them. The house was founded in 1858 by an Englishman, Charles Frederick Worth (1826–96), who secured the patronage of the Empress Eugénie, wife of Napoleon III. Together they set about to revive the French luxury textile industry, Worth fashioning garments from rich and elaborate fabrics and the Empress elegantly displaying the finished products. Not to be outdone in the splendor of their dress, other courts of Europe placed orders with Worth, and business boomed not only for the house but for the entire French textile industry. Charles Frederick retired in the 1880's and turned over the administration of the business to his sons, Jean Philippe and Gaston, and his grandsons, Jean Charles and Jacques; and the younger men continued to advise their clients to wear the most extravagant machine-made fabrics and trimmings.

Representative of the House of Worth is this ice blue silk satin ball gown embellished with woven ribbons and butterflies studded with brilliants. The textile pattern was designed to fit the cut of the dress, so that the butterflies would ascend the panels of the umbrella-shaped skirt. The décolletage, which covers one shoulder and leaves the other bare, is festooned with tulle, velvet ribbon, lace, and artificial flowers.

Gift of Mrs. Paul Pennoyer   65.189.2

Walking Suit

AMERICAN   ABOUT 1896

According to *The American Domestic Cyclopedia,* published in 1890, a morning visit was "paid between the hours of two and four p.m. in the winter and two and five p.m. in the summer." "In receiving morning visitors, it is not necessary that the lady should lay aside the employment in which she may be engaged, particularly if it consists of light or ornamental needlework. Politeness, however, requires that music, drawing or any other occupation that would completely engross the attention, be at once abandoned." The visitor "should be dressed well but not too richly (on a morning visit with carriage at command she may dress more elegantly than if she were on foot)."

For promenading or visiting on Fifth Avenue, this suit of almond green wool crepe with embroidered green velvet and black satin trim would have provided proper attire. The outfit came from a New York City dressmaking establishment run by the Fox sisters. Reputed to be among the finest dressmakers in the city, they were highly selective as to their clientele, refusing commissions if they so pleased. Their skill is seen in the application of decoration, which was used only on the corsage (bodice) of this outfit: a black cummerbund to enhance the illusion of a small waist and a delicate abundance of embroidery on the revers done with an assortment of materials, including cording, chenille, bugle beads, ribbons, jet beads, and silk floss. To help the gored skirt retain its full shape, a horsehair band was incorporated into the lining, and to make sure that the bodice did not suddenly open, hooks and eyes were placed in alternating positions.

Label: Fox / New York

Gift of Miss Mary Louise Deming in memory of her mother, Mrs. Nelson Lloyd Deming   59.40.3

Tea Gown

FRENCH   1903–05

Three generations of Doucets were involved in outfitting the fashionable. The family opened a millinery business in 1815, at a time when machine-made lace was beginning to be used in the adornment of bonnets, and soon an important sideline of their enterprise was to distinguish hand-made lace from the much less valuable bobbin-machine imitations. In time lace was to supercede millinery as the mainstay of the Doucet business. Shortly after the Franco-Prussian War (1870–71), Jacques Doucet, a grandson, was permitted to turn his artistic inclinations to dress design. Gowns from the House of Doucet reflect Jacques' exposure to fine laces and his interest in eighteenth century art.

Edwardian elegance is summed up in this Doucet afternoon dress. Pleated pearl gray chiffon and ribbons of lace, in alternating panels, create a fabric of cloudlike quality that is bound to gravity by the application of horizontal velvet bands. The bodice, boned to conform to the prevailing fashion for a mono-bosom silhouette, takes the form of a bolero jacket with short bell sleeves over long fitted ones. A lining of gray silk taffeta rustles beneath.

This exquisite gown was worn by Louise Bolmer Constable (1861–1928). Her husband, Fredrick Augustus Constable, managed his family's New York dry goods store, Arnold Constable, until his death in 1905.

Label: Doucet

Gift of Mrs. Robert G. Olmsted   65.239.12

Dinner Dress

POSSIBLY FRENCH   ABOUT 1913

Vogue in September 1913 stated: "The principal influences in the new modes are the styles of the period of Louis XIII, the Empire, 1830 and the Second Empire. The silhouette will demand not only flat hips but a flat bust. To accent this many waists will be cut with a low, square corsage [and] a high curved waistline. There is a new tendency in skirts too. Full at the waist they are often draped up in back instead of front. The flaring tunic grows daily in popularity."

Once again a fashion journal has described in generalities a specific period gown. The work of an unknown, but possibly French, dressmaker, this dinner dress combines the open robe style of the seventeenth century with the tubular form popularized in the early years of the nineteenth. The underskirt, of rose chiffon, is embroidered in a rococo swag motif to which are added satin rosettes. The tunic and cummerbund are of rose velvet and the bodice is layered lace. Free-flowing wing-like sleeves are echoed in a small decorative element at the back waistline, a velvet butterfly.

The days of such feminine fashions and fabrics were numbered. World War I was to simplify styles and bring a more masculine appearance to women's clothes.

Gift of Mrs. Howard C. Brokaw   60.167.19

Day Dress

AMERICAN   ABOUT 1918

The years of World War I were quiescent as far as fashion was concerned. Small changes were wrought and recorded in the periodicals, but the real news was being made by nurses, ambulance drivers, and other female war workers. These women found that long, tight skirts were too restrictive; and so skirts were hiked up and hemlines widened. Because the war put an embargo on the production of luxury fabrics and trim, they were abandoned, and garments of simple cut and fabric became modish.

Vogue gave its approval to the use of plainer fabrics in May 1918: "Cotton frocks, though of peasant descent, have climbed into social prominence by their own merits and they are accepted by the very best people this season." "Gingham frocks are inexpensive and require little trimming, as trimming seems out of place with this material. If, however, a trimming is used, it is a piping of plain gingham, collar and cuffs of linen or batiste, pearl buttons or a sash of the material or of ribbon."

This blue and white striped cotton day dress, its flounces stiffened with horsehair bands, was purchased from Thurn, a major dressmaking and importing establishment of conservative taste located on East 52nd Street in New York City.

Gift of Mrs. Albert Gallatin   45.138.2

Tea Gown

AMERICAN   ABOUT 1918–20

The years after World War I witnessed a sharp decline in form-fitting garments and a preference for shorter, fuller skirts. Coats looking very much like capes were modish, and draped garments of vague classical, medieval, and renaissance inspiration were taken up by the followers of Fortuny, Galenga, and Poiret. These three had initiated the fashion for draped garments before the war, but it was fully absorbed only after the conflict.

This tea gown, of taupe velvet and chiffon, is an example of skillful draping. One side panel of the skirt is reminiscent of those formerly incorporated in hobble skirts, while the other falls like an ancient Greek chiton. The flattened bustline and the virtual disappearance of the waistline herald the fashions of the 1920's.

Gift of Mrs. Howard C. Brokaw   60.167.26

Tea Gown and Coat

ITALIAN   ABOUT 1910–39

Subtlety — of line, color, and texture — are the hallmarks of Fortuny gowns and accessories. Mario Fortuny y Madrazo (1871–1949) was of Spanish ancestry. Fascinated by renaissance textiles, he founded a laboratory and work-shop on the island of Giudecca (Venice), where he re-created renaissance motifs and developed the techniques necessary to print them on fabrics. We learn from a 1923 issue of *Vogue* that "the patterns are intricate past all imagining — there must be six hundred and fifty of them" and that "the gold never flecks off from the marvelous velvet." Fortuny's main showroom was in Venice; later there were others in London and New York City.

Year in and year out, from about 1910 through the 1930's, a Fortuny pleated silk satin afternoon dress or tea gown was deemed highly fashionable. Varying slightly, but always drawn from classical Greek models, these garments were known as "Delphos robes." Their colors — ashes of roses, eggshell, apricot, deep turquoise — are soft and rich almost beyond belief.

This apricot gown is composed of three minutely and firmly pleated panels. The sleeves were not cut separately; the only cutting is around the neck. A drawstring embellished with Venetian glass beads runs vertically down the upper sleeve, and a plain drawstring around the neck and another under each arm allow the wearer to fit the gown to her form. A printed belt with the Fortuny imprint came with the dress. The years have proved Fortuny's claim that with proper storage these gowns would not lose their pleats.

The coat is of apricot velvet with a renaissance printed design in silver. Laid flat, it resembles a T with a broad stem. Thus, as with the dress, the coat was shaped by the wearer's body.

Dress gift of Miss Helen Appleton Read   62.170.7
Coat gift of Mrs. Jesse Orrick   66.57.3

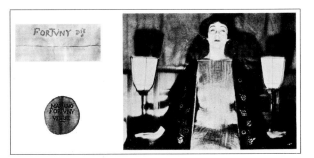

Fortuny labels and contemporary
photograph of Fortuny outfit.
Vogue, May 15, 1923. Copyright
© 1923, renewed 1951.

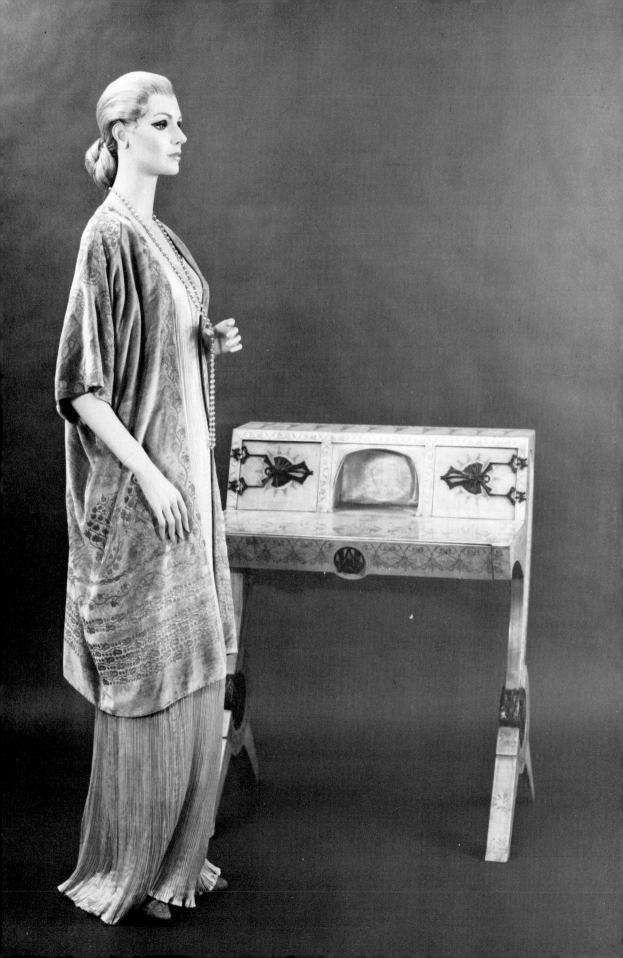

Day Dress

FRENCH 1926

Smartness and tailoring are hallmarks of the creations of Jean Patou. Involved with clothing design from 1914, Patou formed his own establishment after World War I, in 1919, and he controlled it until his death in 1936, when responsibilities were assumed by his brother-in-law. The house was on the Rue Saint-Florentin in Paris. Patou was one of the first Parisian couturiers to experiment with whole-sale copies of original models, a field that was to be fully exploited by later designers.

Although Patou is said not to have favored the "garçonne" (boyish) look advocated by Chanel and some other contemporaries, this afternoon dress does acknowledge the current mode. The dress is a wraparound garment with a sleeveless bodice of café-au-lait crepe and horizontal bands on the skirt of panne velvet in rich chocolate browns. The diagonal line of the V-neck is continued to terminate in a hipline bow that fastens the garment. A beige silk slip came with the dress.

A 1926 Henri Bendel sketchbook illustrates this dress and indicates that it was one of the models the store imported from Paris.

Gift of Mrs. Anthony Wilson   63.227.1a–b

Fashion sketch of Patou
dress imported by Bendel, 1926.

Evening Dress

AMERICAN ABOUT 1929

The stock market wasn't the only thing that fell with a crash in 1929. Jean Patou is perhaps best remembered in costume history as the designer who dropped the hemline on evening gowns in that year, making long dresses fashionable again. Day dresses also were soon lengthened, thus quickly dating and making outré the fashions of the 1920's.

This evening gown of champagne and dark brown satin is a transitional garment, looking back to the no-silhouette silhouette of the 1920's while pointing toward the 1930's with its train and the use of body-shaped bias-cut fabric. The starkness of color and line is emphasized by constructional detail; there are no plackets and the dress must be slipped on over the head. The one break from severity is the bit of drapery falling on the back of the left hip.

A strikingly similar gown was featured in a 1924 issue of *Vogue.* The earlier example came from Callot, a French house noted for the use of elaborate embroideries.

Gift of Mrs. Louis H. Twyeffort   61.110.4

Contemporary photograph of Callot gown. *Vogue,*
November 1, 1924. Copyright © 1924, renewed 1952.

Evening Gown

PROBABLY FRENCH   ABOUT 1934

Through the doors of the Bendel shop on West 57th Street have passed some of the most fashionable women in America. Henri Bendel was born in Lafayette, Louisiana, and began his career as a milliner in New Orleans. He started his first business venture in New York City, Bendel and Sauer, in 1898. Moving to 57th Street in 1913, he made his name as, at one time, the largest American buyer of French model gowns. Among the designers whose creations he imported were Callot, Lanvin, Chanel, Schiaparelli, and Mainbocher.

Bendel's imports about 1934 may have included this evening dress of bias-cut oyster silk crepe with a deep hemline printed in an abstract feather motif in shaded grays. The feathers are elongated as the panel trails to the back. Within the center back of the train are a pair of embroidered eyelets that permit it to be hooked up at the waistline. Thus secured, the train forms a cascade of ruffles down the back of the dress and gives it an even hemline. The sash and the deep V-back neckline, extending to the waist, were fashionable in 1934. The popularity of gowns with trains extended over most of the decade.

Gift of Mrs. V. D. Crisp   63.121.13

Suit

AMERICAN 1942

During the late 1930's and early 1940's women's garments were designed with broad, angular padded shoulders, as if to help the wearer shoulder the troubles of a warring world. Perhaps unconscious too was the preference for navy and white, which, when added to the bold reds of cosmetics, lent a patriotic appearance. This suit by Mme. Eta is of navy rayon crepe. Rolled lapels and three-quarter-length sleeves distinguish the open jacket. A white starched and wired crochet corsage decorates the lapel and repeats the more delicate Irish crochet of the sleeveless bodice. Skirt and bodice are stitched together with an oversash that acts as a cummerbund in front and ties in back with a bow. The skirt is plain except for front panel pleating. Modish accessories include a "doll" hat by Elsa Schiaparelli and crochet gloves.

Born and trained in Hungary, Eta Valer Hentz immigrated to the United States and founded her own dressmaking business, Ren-Eta Gowns, Inc., which catered to the higher priced wholesale trade. As head designer, "Mme. Eta" presided over the establishment, located at 498 Seventh Avenue, New York City, in the heart of the American dressmaking industry.

Gift of Mme. Eta   44.95.13

Sketches by Mme. Eta for suit, 1942.

Street Dress

FRENCH 1949

Contrasts in skirt dimensions were conspicuous in postwar dress design. The extremes were represented by very slim and by very full flared examples. In both cases the hemline was lengthened, a result of the lifting of wartime restrictions on fabric use.

This tailored street dress was designed by Pierre Balmain, who opened his salon at Rue François Premier 44, Paris, in 1945 and hit his stride in the late 1940's. The bodice is cut with a semi-bolero that hangs free in the back and features a white piqué collar, tie, and cuffs. To allow the wearer to walk, the pencil-slim skirt has a deep hemline vent with matching fabric underneath. The fabric is a worsted type black and white stepped twill made from Teca estron and rayon.

Gift of A. M. Tenny Corporation   50.56.7

Contemporary fashion photograph

Coat

FRENCH   1950

The fashion stagnation of the war years was swept aside by a relatively unknown Parisian designer named Christian Dior with the showing of his 1947 spring collection. His outfits created an electrifying "new look." Hemlines dropped, skirts flared, waists were cinched in, hips emphasized, and shoulders rounded. This black winter coat sums up all of Dior's innovations. Headlined "The Oblique Collar" in the September 1, 1950, issue of *Vogue,* the coat is cut along "princess" lines and is a "swinging redingote," being buttoned from the neck to just below the waist. Raglan sleeves and padded hips emphasize the drawn-in waist. The collar, set low on the shoulders like a cape, makes a "beautiful arch of a collar, rolled high . . . slanted from armhole to jutting point."

Christian Dior, who maintained his fashion preeminence to the end of his life, was trained by Robert Piguet and Lucien Lelong. After his death in 1957, his house was ably administered by two of his protégés, Yves St. Laurent and Marc Bohan.

Gift of Mrs. Jeane Eddy   61.137

Contemporary photograph of "Oblique Collar" coat. *Vogue,* September 1, 1950. Copyright © 1950.

Day Dress

FRENCH ABOUT 1950

Jacques Griffe was trained by the master of bias-cut gowns, Madeleine Vionnet. He in turn applied his background to this one-piece dress of beige wool jersey. Everywhere the dress clings to the form: around the throat, across the bodice, down the full length of the sleeves, and swirling around the waist and hips. The draping is broken twice by deep pockets, one on the chest and another on the back of the left hip. Because the draped design runs diagonally, the back zippered closing too assumes an off-center position.

Women's garments of the early 1950's were the antithesis of those of the 1920's. They fitted the form like a glove, emphasizing the bust and hip lines by drawing in the waist. Colors were somber: beige and gray, dark greens and blues.

Gift of Miss Joan Fontaine   62.91.2

Day Dress

AMERICAN ABOUT 1955

A booming post-war economy that produced new labor-saving devices also created an expanding market for garments suitable for leisure wear. Fashion became more casual; even gowns for formal functions were given street-length hemlines.

Middy blouses and bodices had been popular around the turn of the century, and now at mid-century they returned to favor, along with full skirts supported by crinoline petticoats. This dress, of tan silk with a navy polka dot imprint, has a sleeveless bodice with a wide sailor collar over a bow tie. The unpressed knife-pleated skirt has an attached petticoat made of horsehair bands.

The dress bears a Traina-Norell label. Anthony Traina and Norman Norell were partners from 1941 to 1960. During this period they — along with Pauline Trigère, Claire McCardell, Adrian, James Galanos, and others — began to draw fashion-conscious American women away from the European salons toward the serious support of American designers.

Gift of Miss Lauren Bacall   62.186.12a–c

Suit

AMERICAN   ABOUT 1960

Two rich colors, coal black and chocolate brown, become even richer when they are skillfully united. This three-piece suit of brown wool trimmed with black braid and buttons, with a black satin blouse, was created by the dean of American designers, Norman Norell. Norell received his early training at two New York City design schools, Parsons and Pratt. He worked for Hattie Carnegie from 1928 until 1940, when he formed a partnership with a tailor, Anthony Traina, which lasted until 1960. It was Norell who provided the creative flair for the association, while Traina provided the technical knowledge.

This box jacket illustrates two hallmarks of Norell design, a shallow V-neck and double-breasted tailoring. The symmetry and angularity of the jacket are not echoed in the blouse, which has an off-center front closing accentuated by a bow at the neckline and a tape that gathers in the waistline fullness. The skirt fullness is gathered in the back between two zippers that rest on the hips.

Gift of Miss Lauren Bacall   67.245.37a–c

Day Dress

FRENCH   ABOUT 1965

Navy and white cotton piqué make a crisp combination in this mini-skirted A-line dress from the French couturier André Courrèges.

After training under Balenciaga for eleven years, Courrèges set up his own house in 1961 at Avenue Kléber 48, Paris, moving in 1966 to Rue François Premier 40. His spring collection of 1964 introduced fashion to the Space Age by emphasizing the use of plastics and incorporating bold colors and cut-out motifs in his designs. As in this dress, Courrèges likes to play his color choice against a white background.

In 1966 Courrèges designed a collection called "Couture Future," consisting of ready-to-wear items that had been produced in his own workrooms. Thus he attempted to bring the long-standing French couture tradition into line with the contemporary boutique idiom.

Gift of Miss Mildred Custin   70.182.6

Photography by Scott Hyde and Richard Di Liberto
Type set by The Brooklyn Museum Press
Printed by Sanders Printing Corporation, New York City